50 FILM TUNES FOR ALTO SAX
GRADED

Published by
Wise Publications
14-15 Berners Street, London W1T 3LJ, UK.

Exclusive Distributors:
Music Sales Limited
Distribution Centre, Newmarket Road,
Bury St Edmunds, Suffolk IP33 3YB, UK.
Music Sales Corporation
257 Park Avenue South, New York, NY 10010, USA.
Music Sales Pty Limited
20 Resolution Drive, Caringbah, NSW 2229, Australia.

Order No. AM997887
ISBN 978-1-84938-135-2
This book © Copyright 2009 Wise Publications,
a division of Music Sales Limited.

Edited by Jenni Wheeler.
Music processed by Camden Music.
Printed in the EU.

Your Guarantee of Quality
As publishers, we strive to produce every book to
the highest commercial standards.
This book has been carefully designed to minimise awkward
page turns and to make playing from it a real pleasure.
Particular care has been given to specifying acid-free, neutral-sized
paper made from pulps which have not been elemental chlorine bleached.
This pulp is from farmed sustainable forests and
was produced with special regard for the environment.
Throughout, the printing and binding have been planned to ensure
a sturdy, attractive publication which should give years of enjoyment.
If your copy fails to meet our high standards,
please inform us and we will gladly replace it.

www.musicsales.com

WISE PUBLICATIONS
part of The Music Sales Group

London / New York / Paris / Sydney / Copenhagen / Berlin / Madrid / Tokyo

GRADING NOTES

The pieces in this book have been carefully graded according to
various criteria such as rhythmic complexity, phrasing, tempo, key, range, etc.
Look for the number of stars for each piece to give you
an idea of the approximate playing level.
All musicians have particular strengths and weaknesses,
so the grading offered here should be taken as a suggestion only.

Generally, pieces with one star have simple rhythms,
straight forward phrasings and few difficult intervals;
essentially diatonic and in easier keys.

Pieces with two stars will have more challenging passages,
perhaps containing more rhythmic complexity,
more advanced key signatures and possibly explore a wider
range on the instrument.

Three-star pieces may include chromaticism,
challenging articulation and more advanced positioning.
Read through rhythms and keys before playing, and check for
time-signature changes and correct phrasing.

All Love Can Be
(from 'A Beautiful Mind')

Words by Will Jennings & Music by James Horner

Baby Elephant Walk
(from 'Hatari!')

Music by Henry Mancini

Back To The Future (Theme)
(from 'Back To The Future')

Music by Alan Silvestri

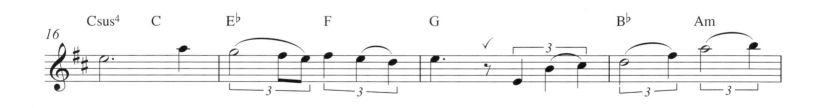

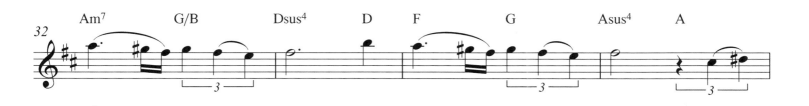

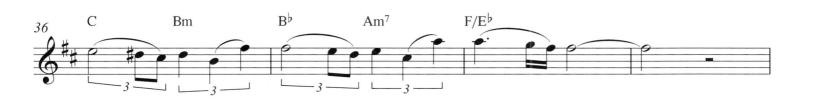

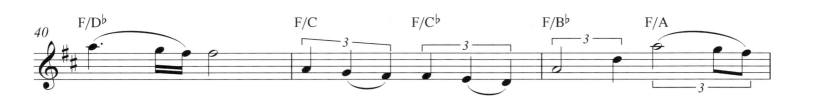

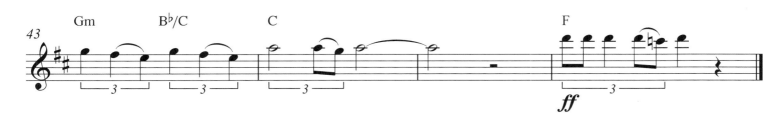

Betty et Zorg
(from 'Betty Blue')

Music by Gabriel Yared

Build Me Up Buttercup
(from 'There's Something About Mary')

Words & Music by Michael D'Abo & Tony Macaulay

Blue Velvet
(from 'Blue Velvet')

Words & Music by Bernie Wayne & Lee Morris

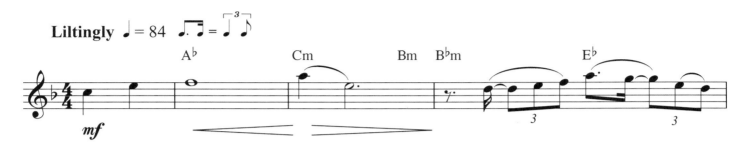

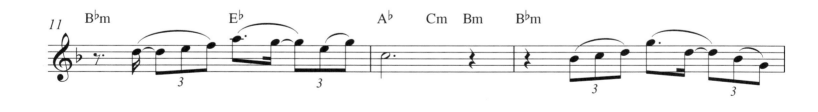

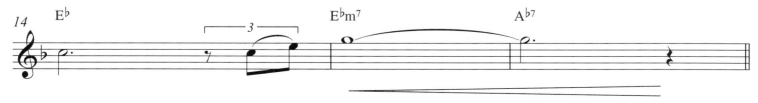

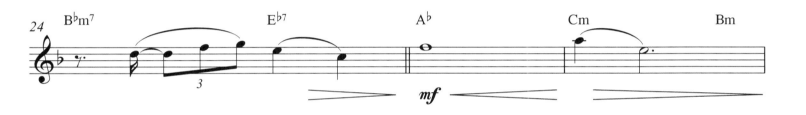

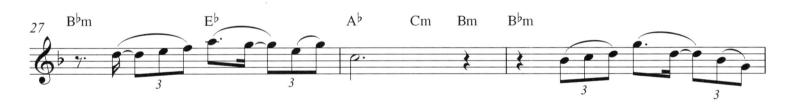

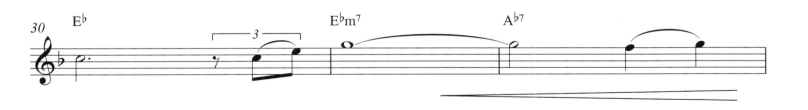

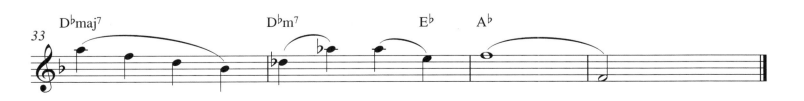

Circle Of Life
(from Walt Disney Pictures' 'The Lion King')

Words by Tim Rice & Music by Elton John

Clair De Lune
(from 'Ocean's 11')

Music by Claude Debussy

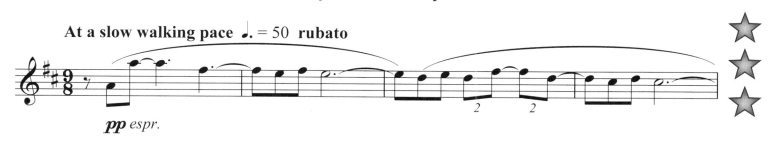

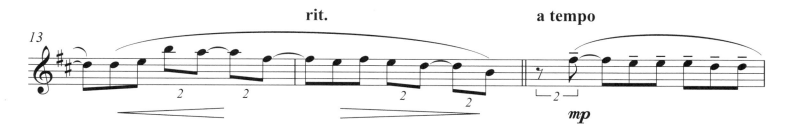

poco rit.

with more movement

p

pushing forward

mp   *mf*

more calmly

molto dim.   *pp*

p

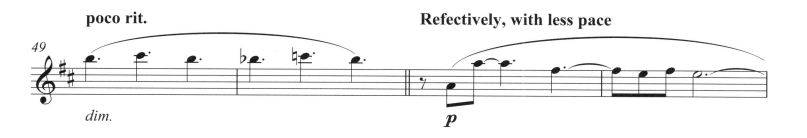

poco rit.

Refectively, with less pace

dim.

p

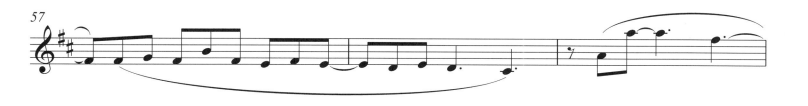

moving on

rit.

moving on

rit. al fine

Come What May
(from 'Moulin Rouge')

Words & Music by David Baerwald

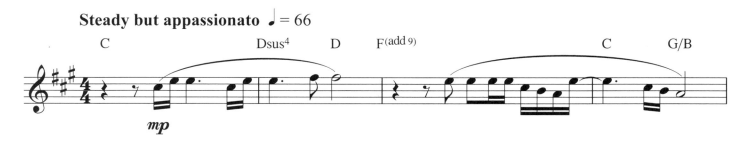

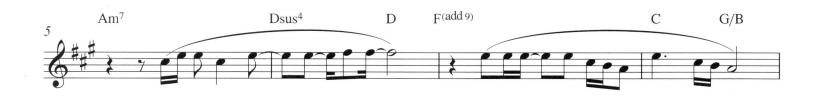

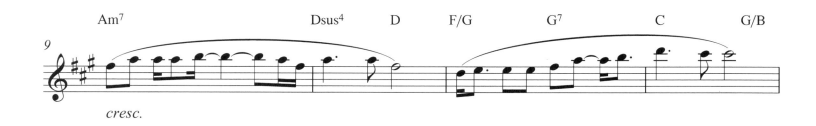

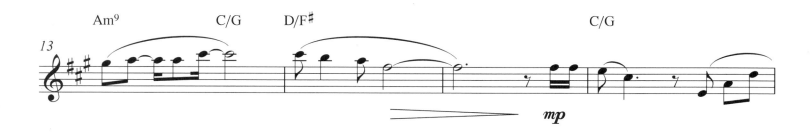

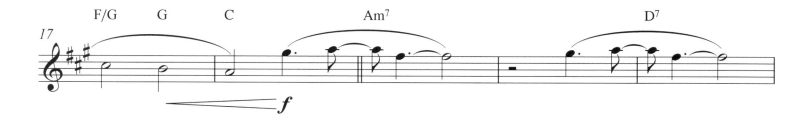

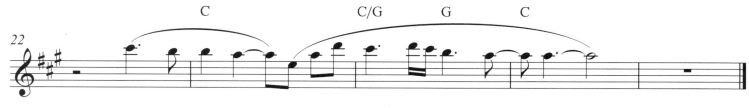

18

GoldenEye
(from 'GoldenEye')

Words & Music by Bono & The Edge

Menacingly ♩ = 102

Dancing With The Bear
(from 'Finding Neverland')

Music by Jan A.P. Kaczmarek

22

Miller's Crossing (End Titles)
(from 'Miller's Crossing')

Music by Carter Burwell

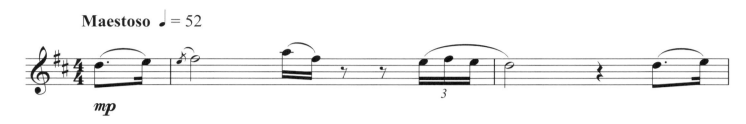

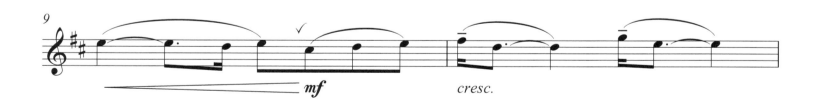

Eye Of The Tiger
(from 'Rocky III')

Words & Music by Frank Sullivan III & Jim Peterik

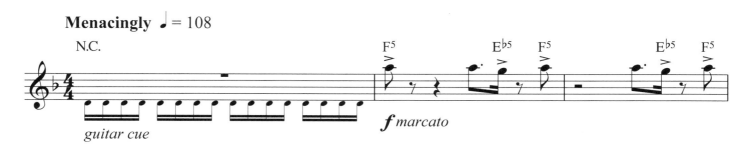

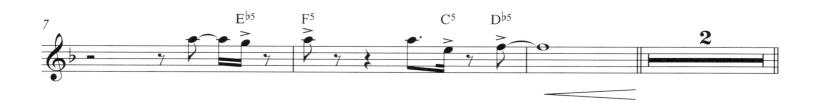

Georgia On My Mind
(from 'Ray')

Words by Stuart Gorrell & Music by Hoagy Carmichael

A Hard Day's Night
(from 'A Hard Day's Night')

Words & Music by John Lennon & Paul McCartney

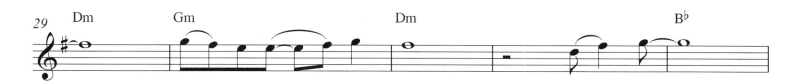

Slower

He's A Pirate

(from 'Pirates Of The Caribbean: The Curse Of The Black Pearl')

Music by Klaus Badelt

Honor Him/Now We Are Free
(from 'Gladiator')

Music by Hans Zimmer

HONOR HIM

Noble and grand ♩ = 66

mp with a full tone, espr.

NOW WE ARE FREE

♩ = 69

fade in   (Strings cue)   **5**   *mp dreamily*

I Had A Farm In Africa
(Main Title from 'Out Of Africa')

Music by John Barry

Into The West

(from 'The Lord Of The Rings: The Return Of The King')

Words & Music by Annie Lennox, Howard Shore & Fran Walsh

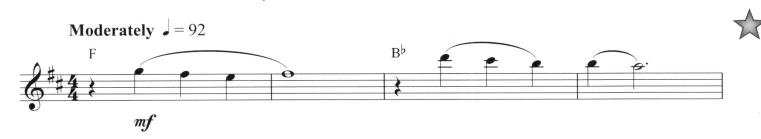

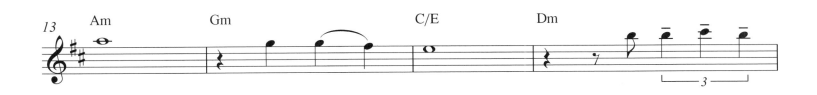

(I've Had) The Time Of My Life
(from 'Dirty Dancing')

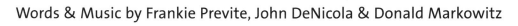

Words & Music by Frankie Previte, John DeNicola & Donald Markowitz

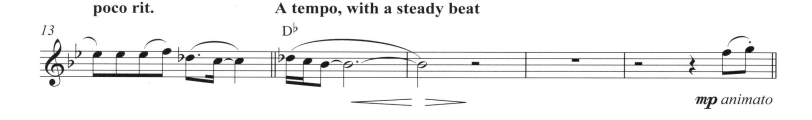

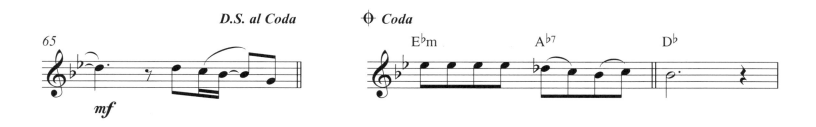

Lawrence Of Arabia (Main Titles)
(from 'Lawrence Of Arabia')

Music by Maurice Jarre

Le Banquet/La Valse Des Monstres
(from 'Amélie')

Music by Yann Tiersen

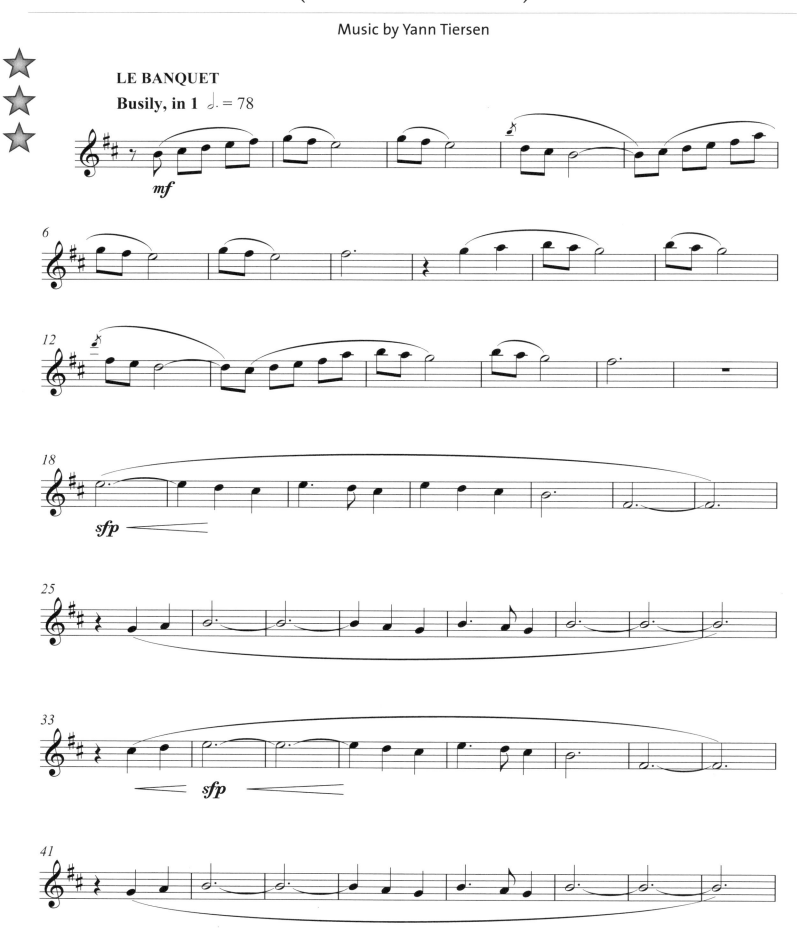

LA VALSE DES MONSTRES

A little faster

To Coda ⊕

44

Licence To Kill
(from 'Licence To Kill')

Words & Music by John Barry, Leslie Bricusse, Anthony Newley, Narada Michael Walden, Walter Afanasieff & Jeffrey Cohen

Live To Tell
(from 'At Close Range')

Words & Music by Madonna Ciccone & Pat Leonard

A Love Before Time
(from 'Crouching Tiger, Hidden Dragon')

Words & Music by James Schamus, Tan Dun & Jorge Calandrelli

Love Is All Around
(from 'Four Weddings And A Funeral')

Words & Music by Reg Presley

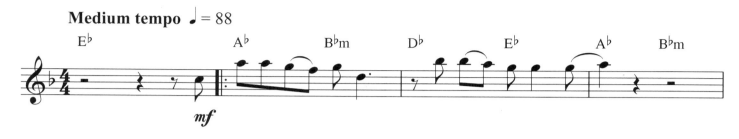

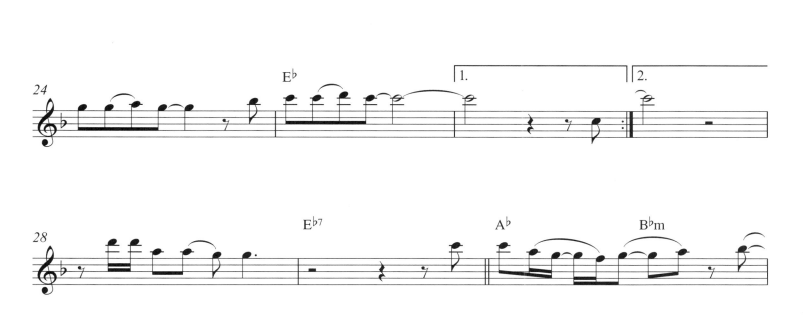

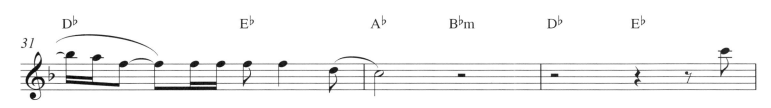

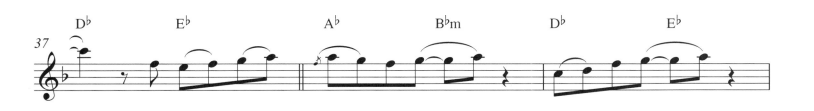

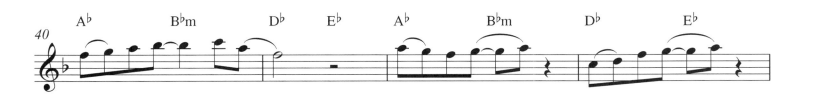

A Man And A Woman
(from 'Un Homme et une Femme')

Words by Pierre Barouh & Music by Francis Lai. English Translation by Jerry Keller

(Straight quavers)

Mothersbaugh's Canon
(from 'The Royal Tenenbaums')

Music by Mark Mothersbaugh

Slowly and thoughtfully ♩ = 63

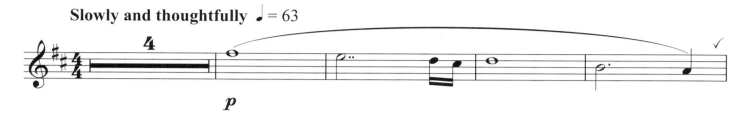

58

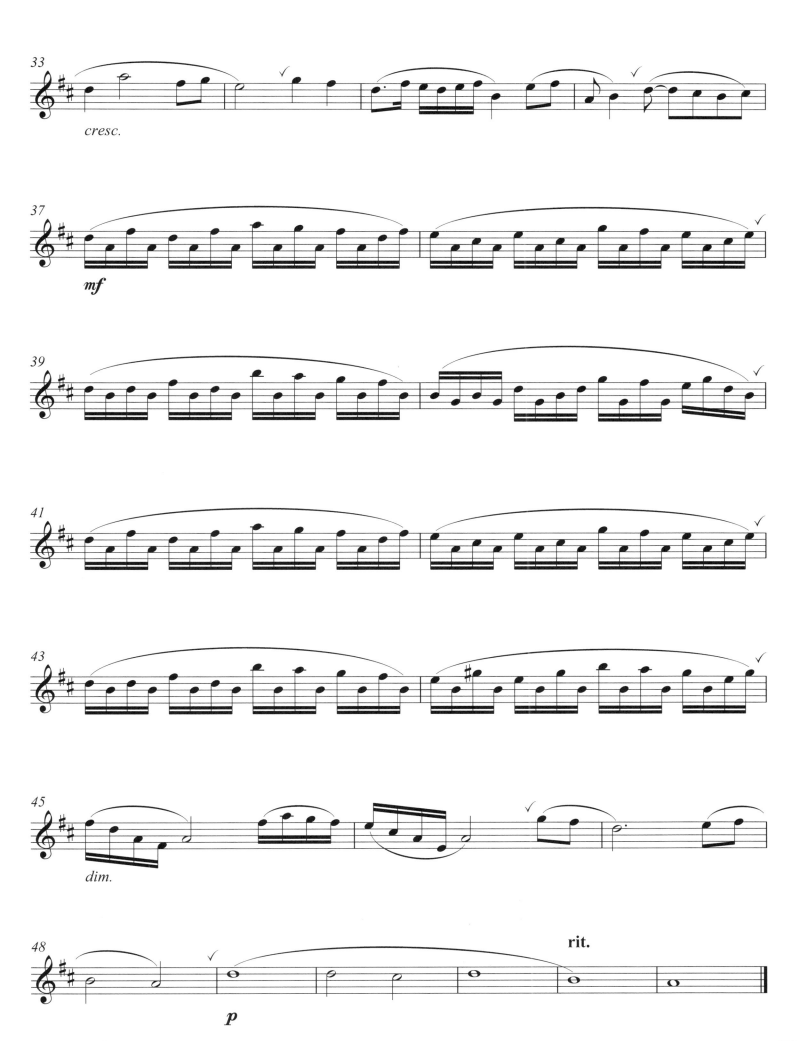

Nothing's Gonna Stop Us Now
(from 'Mannequin')

Words & Music by Diane Warren & Albert Hammond

Oh, Pretty Woman
(from 'Pretty Woman')

Words & Music by Roy Orbison & Bill Dees

Once Upon A Time In The West
(from 'Once Upon A Time In The West')

Music by Ennio Morricone

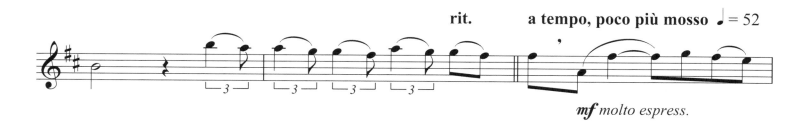

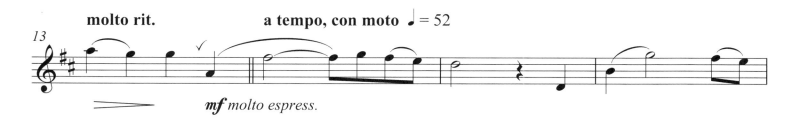

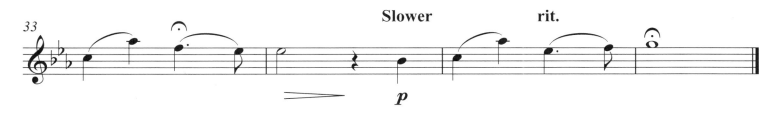

Passage Of Time/Vianne Sets Up Shop
(from The Miramax Motion Picture 'Chocolat')

Music by Rachel Portman

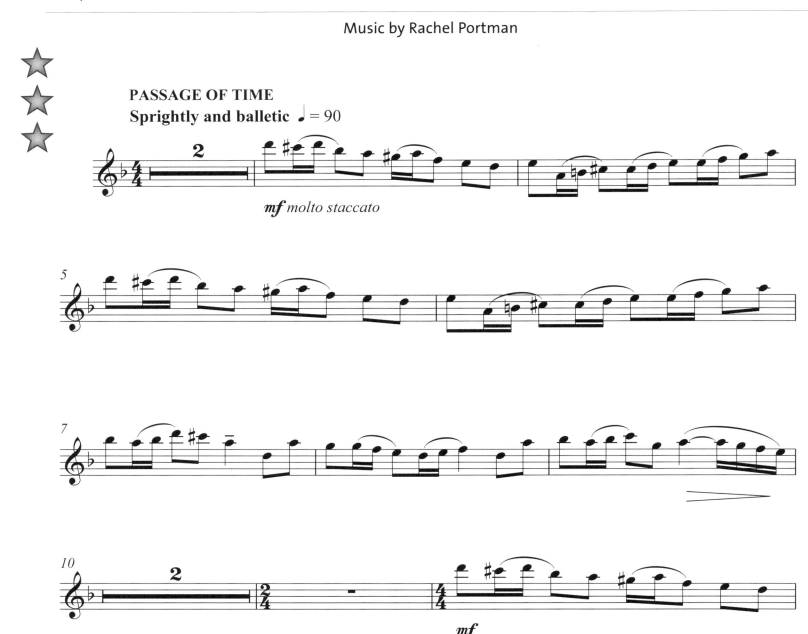

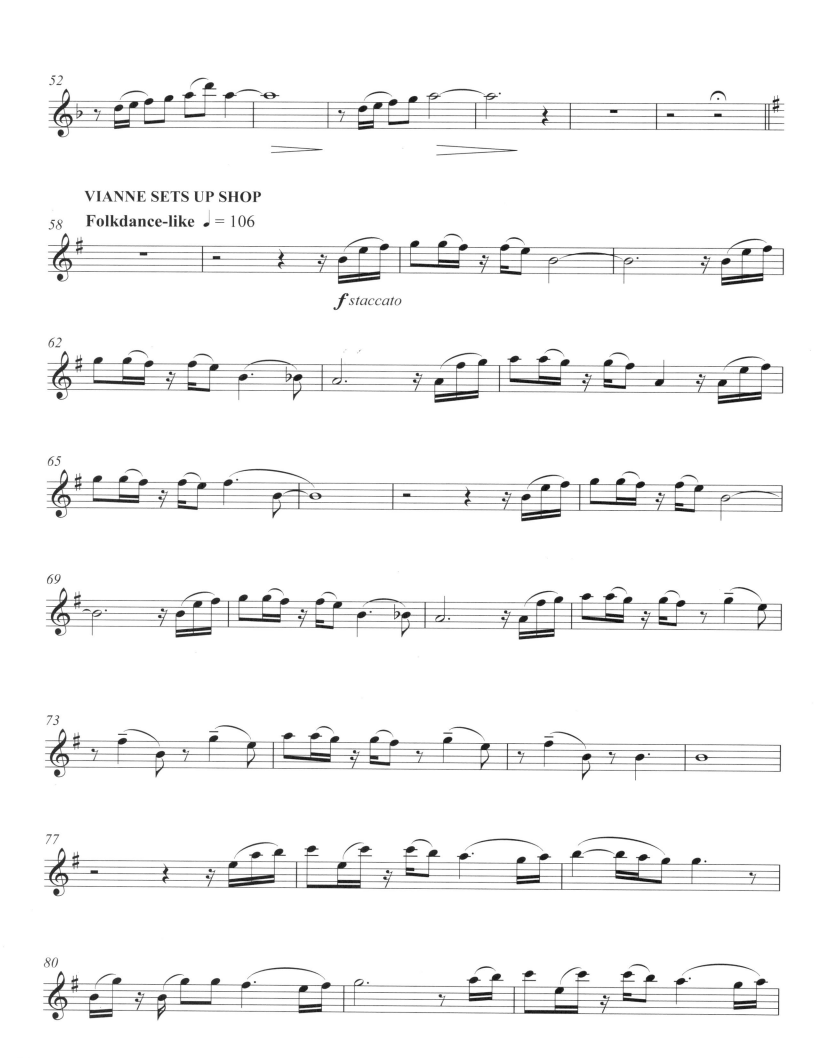

VIANNE SETS UP SHOP

Pelagia's Song
(from 'Captain Corelli's Mandolin')

Music by Stephen Warbeck

Sadly, tenderly, freely ♩ = 80 **rubato**

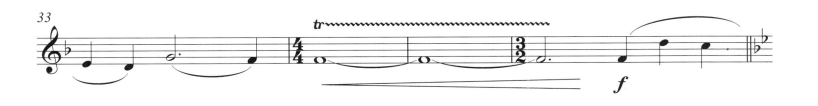

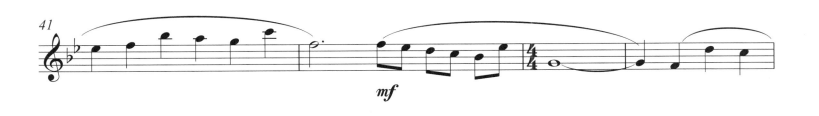

Pelle Erobreren
(from 'Pelle The Conqueror')

Music by Stefan Nilsson

Prologue: My Life Before Me
(from 'The Portrait Of A Lady')

Music by Wojciech Kilar

PM's Love Theme
(from 'Love Actually')

Words & Music by Craig Armstrong

With statesman-like gravitas ♩ = 80

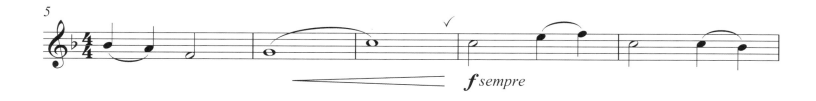

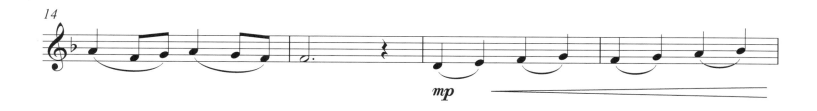

The Promise
(from 'The Piano')

Music by Michael Nyman

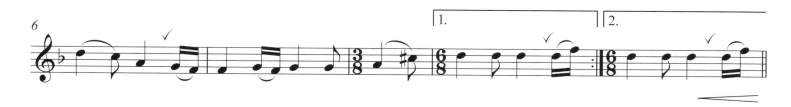

74

Schindler's List (Theme)
(from 'Schindler's List')

Music by John Williams

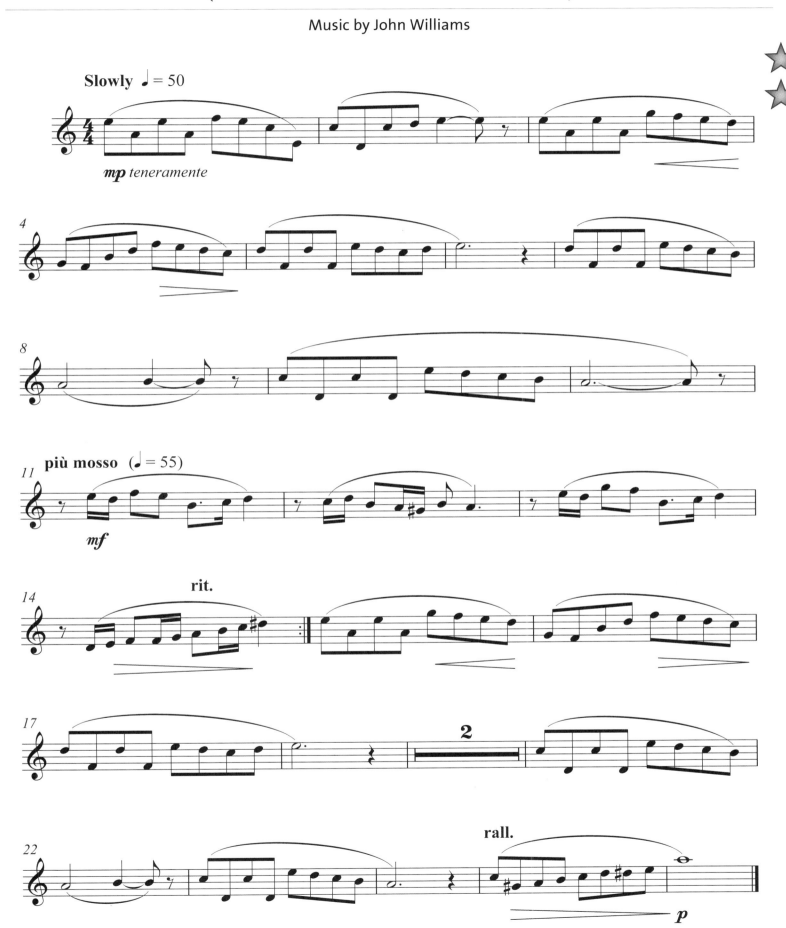

Reprise...
(from 'Spirited Away')

Music by Joe Hisaishi

dim. poco a poco

Rule The World
(from 'Stardust')

Words & Music by Mark Owen, Gary Barlow, Jason Orange & Howard Donald

Scene D'Amour
(from 'Vertigo')

Music by Bernard Herrmann

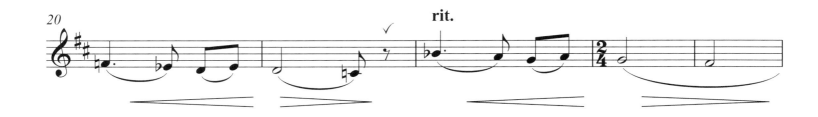

The Shower
(from 'Dressed To Kill')

Music by Pino Donaggio

82

mp espressivo

mf

mf

The Sound Of Silence
(from 'The Graduate')

Words & Music by Paul Simon

Top Gun (Anthem)
(from 'Top Gun')

Music by Harold Faltermeyer

Sweets To The Sweet—Farewell
(from 'Hamlet')

Music by Patrick Doyle

Try A Little Tenderness
(from 'The Commitments')

Words & Music by Harry Woods, Jimmy Campbell & Reg Connelly

Up Where We Belong
(from 'An Officer And A Gentleman')

Words & Music by Jack Nitzsche, Will Jennings & Buffy Sainte-Marie

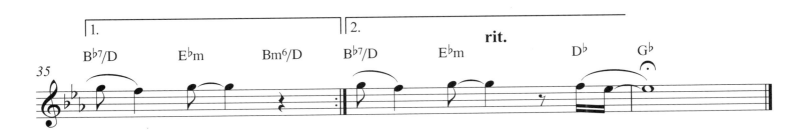

Voulez-Vous
(from 'Mamma Mia!')

Words & Music by Benny Andersson & Björn Ulvaeus

A Whole New World
(from 'Aladdin')

Words by Tim Rice & Music by Alan Menken

You Know My Name
(Theme from 'James Bond: Casino Royale')

Words & Music by David Arnold & Chris Cornell

Energetically, with a strong rock beat ♩ = 136

94

123456789